Barbie

Barbie

CONTENTS

FUTURE IS BRIGHT

Barbie

Barbie

Barbie™

ANNUAL 2023

Published 2022.
Little Brother Books Ltd, Ground Floor,
23 Southernhay East, Exeter, Devon EX1 1QL
books@littlebrotherbooks.co.uk | www.littlebrotherbooks.co.uk

Printed in China. Xuantan Temple Industrial Zone, Gulao Town,
Heshan, Guangdong.

The Little Brother Books trademark, email and website addresses,
are the sole and exclusive properties of Little Brother Books Limited.

Barbie

MY WORLD: Barbie™

MY WORLD!

Full Name: Barbie Roberts

Also known as: Malibu!

Where I live: Right now I am rocking it in New York!

My favourite things: Music, vlogging, tech, my friends and, of course, my family!

My Parents

Full Name: Margaret Roberts

Job: Computer engineer (although she used to be a writer!)

About: Barbie's mum is fun, imaginative and supportive. She loves solving problems and helping her daughters to achieve their dreams, as well as chasing her own!

Full Name: George Richard Carlos Roberts

Job: Documentary Maker

About: Barbie's dad is fascinated by the world around him. He loves asking questions about the world and learning - something he's passed on to Barbie!

MY SISTERS

Full Name: Skipper

About: Barbie's eldest little sister is super-smart and super cool. She loves gadgets and fashion, but most of all she adores her little pup, DJ.

Full Name: Stacie

About: Stacie is sporty, enthusiastic and loves her sisters. She loves trying new things and isn't afraid to get things wrong – after all, that's the best way to get better!

Full Name: Chelsea

About: This baby sister is anything but a baby. Just like Dad, she is interested in the world and wants to discover as much as she can, even if it gets her into mischief sometimes!

MY FRIENDS

Nikki: Arty, creative and totally unique

Daisy: Music-loving superstar DJ with a big heart

Teresa: Intelligent, level-headed and always reliable

Renee: Lives life on super-speed and is never without her board.

Ken: Barbie's oldest friend. He loves everything about the ocean: swimming in it, riding on it and studying what lives in it!

MY WORLD: YOU!

Now it's over to you! Use these headlines and spaces to write down everything that is important to you!

MY WORLD!

Name: Nya dawda

Birthday: 19th June

Some of my favourite things: art, fashion, football, Racing, daily mile, reading, clothes, accsesories, food and stage coach.

Draw a picture of yourself here!

My Family

is active, creative and suny. My family has four favrite sport football, net ball, volly ball and cricet. They are all ful of love and loves give cuddes. There so positive and helpful.

> Your **family** can be whoever you want it to be, your parents, grandparents, or anyone **special** who lives with you.

MY FRIENDS

Name: Akshaya

Fun fact about them: She loves to sing in a high voice

Name: Lakshineye

Fun fact about them: loves to danes in her culture

Name: Sara

Fun fact about them: she love to be sasy like me

My Hobbies

A hobby is anything you love to do in your free time, from reading to jet skiing!

1. drawing fashoin
2. gymnastics
3. Ice skate evean when I am not on ice
4. make mosaics on the computer and sell it
5. make word art on the computer and selli

My pets

Draw a picture of your pet here!
If you don't have one, draw the pet you'd love to have one day.

MY FAVOURITE MUSIC

1. Holiday
2. labric grove
3. Just like a woman
4. fantasy
5. woman
7. black magic

Mindful moments

Feeling overwhelmed or worried about something happens to everyone from time to time. These pages will show you simple ways to calm your mind and relax your body!

Mindful breathing

These breathing techniques are great at anytime – even when you are surrounded by people!

The 3 second method

This breathing practice is good for calming nerves!

 Close your eyes and breath in slowly through your nose for three seconds.

 Hold your breath for three seconds.

Breathe out slowly though your mouth for three seconds.

The loud *sigh*

This practice is good if you are feeling upset or frustrated.

 Breath in through your nose for four seconds.

Hold your breath for two seconds.

Now let out your breath while making a noise or saying a word. Some people say Ha! or Huh!

The louder you exhale, the better you should feel! Repeat two or three times.

The *blowing* wind

This practice is good for clearing a worried mind.

Stand with your legs hip-width apart.

Repeat the steps for the 3-second method a couple of times.

As you breathe in, think of anything that is worrying you. It can be anything from something big to something that only matters to you.

As you breathe out, take a step forward with one leg. At the same time, use your arms to 'push' away your worries.

Take a step back and repeat. Do this a couple of times to really clear your mind.

Did you know:
Breathing techniques are used all over the world as a way to improve physical and mental health.

Animal Care

Colour in this picture of Malibu and Brooklyn as they learn how to be a vet!

TEXT MESSAGE MATCH

Malibu and Brooklyn have mixed up their messages! Can you put them in the correct order?

1

> Our new stage outfits! — 3
>
> Hey Malibu! Rafa said to meet at the cafe at 1pm. He has exciting news? — 1
>
> Ooh what is it? — 2
>
> Can't wait to look fabulous! — 4

BROOKLYN'S PHONE

2

> Why? — 1
>
> 3pm, but we have to be quick! — 2
>
> Hey Brooklyn what time is the studio booked? — M
>
> We only have it until 4pm! — 4

MALIBU'S PHONE

Answers on page 76

ECO FASHION

If you **love fashion** and the **environment** – you've come to the right place! Here's how to make your wardrobe fabulously eco-friendly.

Shop vintage!

This doesn't mean spending lots on designer labels! Instead, check out your local charity shop or vintage store. You could even see if an older relative has anything they don't want any more.

Get sewing

If your favourite top has a rip or tear, ask a grown up to show you how to sew it back together. For bigger holes, sew a patch of fun fabric or a patch over the top.

Barbie

Have a swapping party

Ask your friends to bring over any clothes they have grown out of or got bored of wearing. Put them all in a big pile and have a rummage to find your next favourite item.

Did you know?
In the UK, over 300,000 tonnes of old clothes are dumped each year.

Customise

If you have a top or pair of jeans you no longer like or have grown out of, don't throw them away! Adding a patch, some embroidery or turning jeans into a skirt are all great ways of customising old clothes.

Try adding sequins to an old hoody!

Did you know?
It takes 7,500 litres of water to make one pair of jeans?

BE YOU

Barbie

FRIENDSHIP FLIPPED!

Take a look at this picture of Brooklyn and Malibu — something's not quite right! Rearrange the strips into the correct order.

Answers on page 76

1 **2** **3** **4** **5** **6**

....

ENERGY BITES

These easy, no-bake bites are great for when you need a healthy boost!

INGREDIENTS

- 100g of your choice of nuts (unsalted)
- 75g raisin or sultanas
- 1 tbsp cocoa powder
- 1 tbsp maple syrup or honey
- 50g desiccated coconut
- 2 tbsp smooth or crunchy peanut butter

WHAT TO DO

!
Ask a grown-up to help.

1 Place all your ingredients (apart from the coconut) into a food processor and mix until they are combined into one dough.

2 If you don't have a processor, carefully chop the nuts and dried fruit into small pieces, then mix all the ingredients by hand until they are combined.

DID YOU KNOW?
Raisin and sultanas are good for your tummy!

3 Take pieces of the mixture and roll into balls, about the size of a ping-pong ball.

4 Roll the balls in desiccated coconut so they have a light layer all over.

TIP
Add 1 tbsp of chai seeds to make your bites extra healthy!

5 Place onto baking paper on a baking tray and place in the fridge.

6 After 20 minutes they are ready to eat!

GONE to the DOGS

Brooklyn and Malibu have to think of a way to get money, fast, if they are ever going to record their new song. Read this story, then use the words from the word bank on this page to fill in the blanks!

WORD BANK

$150	fashion	money	song
Brooklyn	fast	one	Speaker
cats	food	pay	stage
chasing	happy	Rafa	time
demo	help	school	walk
dogs	leave	show	walking
door	Malibu	smiled	York

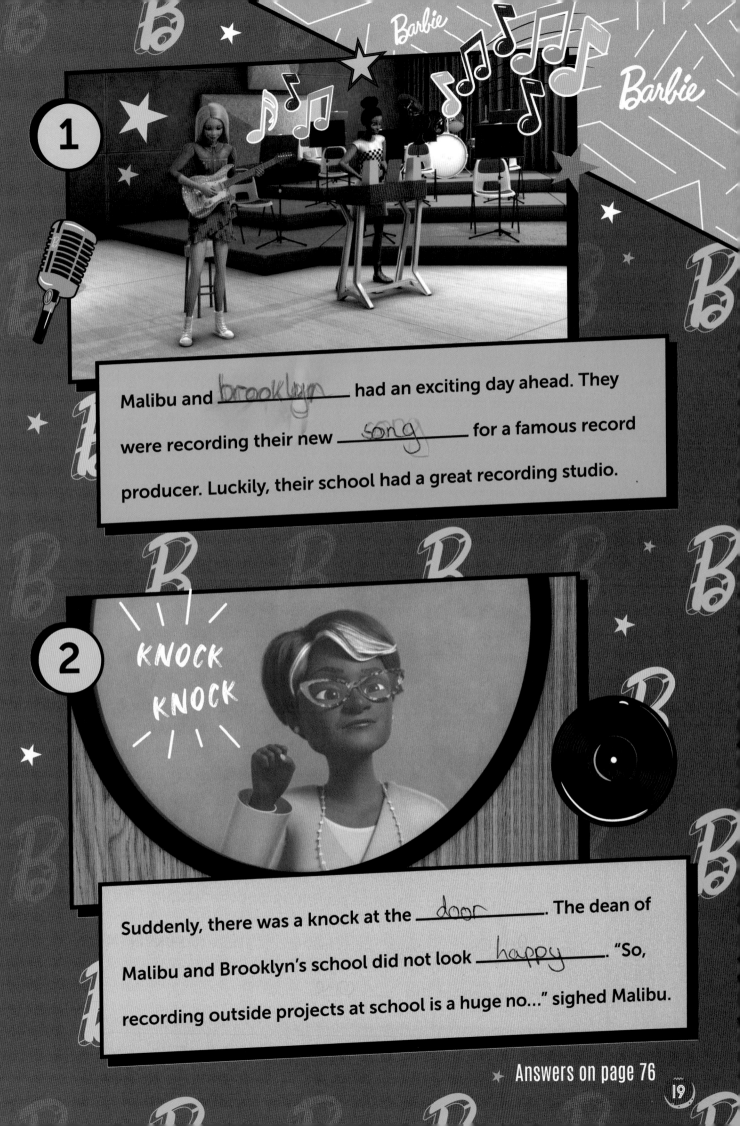

1

Malibu and _brooklyn_ had an exciting day ahead. They were recording their new _song_ for a famous record producer. Luckily, their school had a great recording studio.

2

KNOCK KNOCK

Suddenly, there was a knock at the _door_. The dean of Malibu and Brooklyn's school did not look _happy_. "So, recording outside projects at school is a huge no..." sighed Malibu.

Answers on page 76

3

"We definitely need a new plan for recording our _demo_

song," said Malibu. "Um, you're in New _york_ City,"

said Rafa. "I'm sure you can find another studio."

4

Brooklyn and Malibu began to search for another studio. "It's just

like _Rafa_ said," said Brooklyn. "There are plenty of

studios. How about this _one_?"

5

Brooklyn looked up the details of Blown Speaker Studios.

It didn't look quite as luxurious as the one they were used

to at _~~speaker~~ school_. "Come on," said _~~limited~~ malibu_,

cheerfully. "Looks can be deceiving!"

Answers on page 76

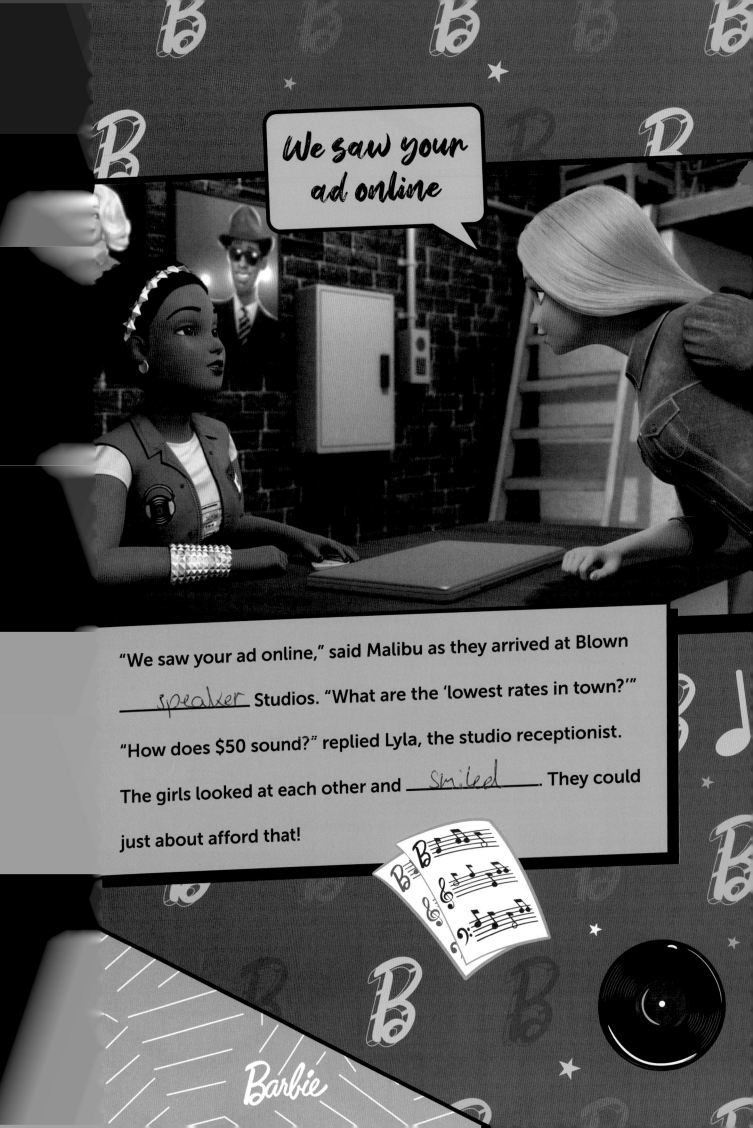

"We saw your ad online," said Malibu as they arrived at Blown

_____speaker_____ Studios. "What are the 'lowest rates in town?'"

"How does $50 sound?" replied Lyla, the studio receptionist.

The girls looked at each other and ___smiled___. They could

just about afford that!

7

After three hours recording their song, Brooklyn and Malibu were getting ready to ___leave___. "That'll be $150," said Lyla. "You said it was $50!" replied Brooklyn, shocked. "$50 an hour," replied Lyla. "That makes ___$150___."

8

Brooklyn and Malibu had to make $150, and ___fast___. Luckily, Rafa had a plan. "I've been too busy with my charity fashion show to take Gato for a ___walk___," he said. "Why don't you work for me?"

Answers on page 76

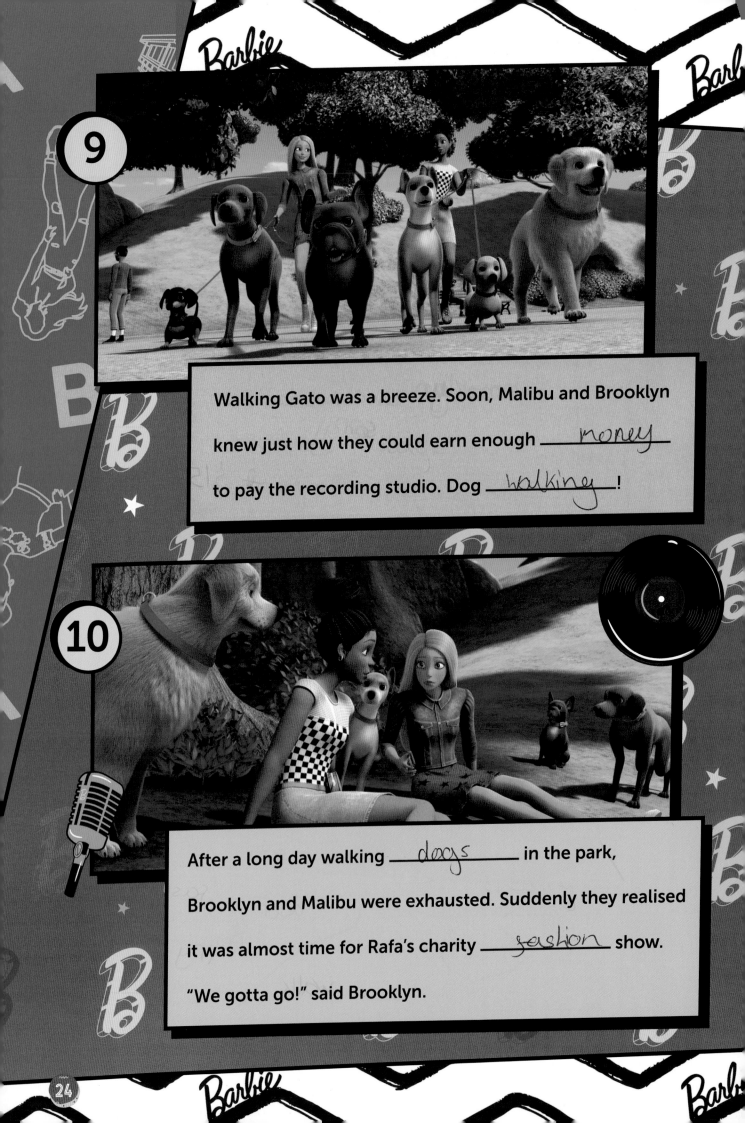

9

Walking Gato was a breeze. Soon, Malibu and Brooklyn knew just how they could earn enough ___money___

to pay the recording studio. Dog ___walking___!

10

After a long day walking ___dogs___ in the park,

Brooklyn and Malibu were exhausted. Suddenly they realised

it was almost time for Rafa's charity ___fashion___ show.

"We gotta go!" said Brooklyn.

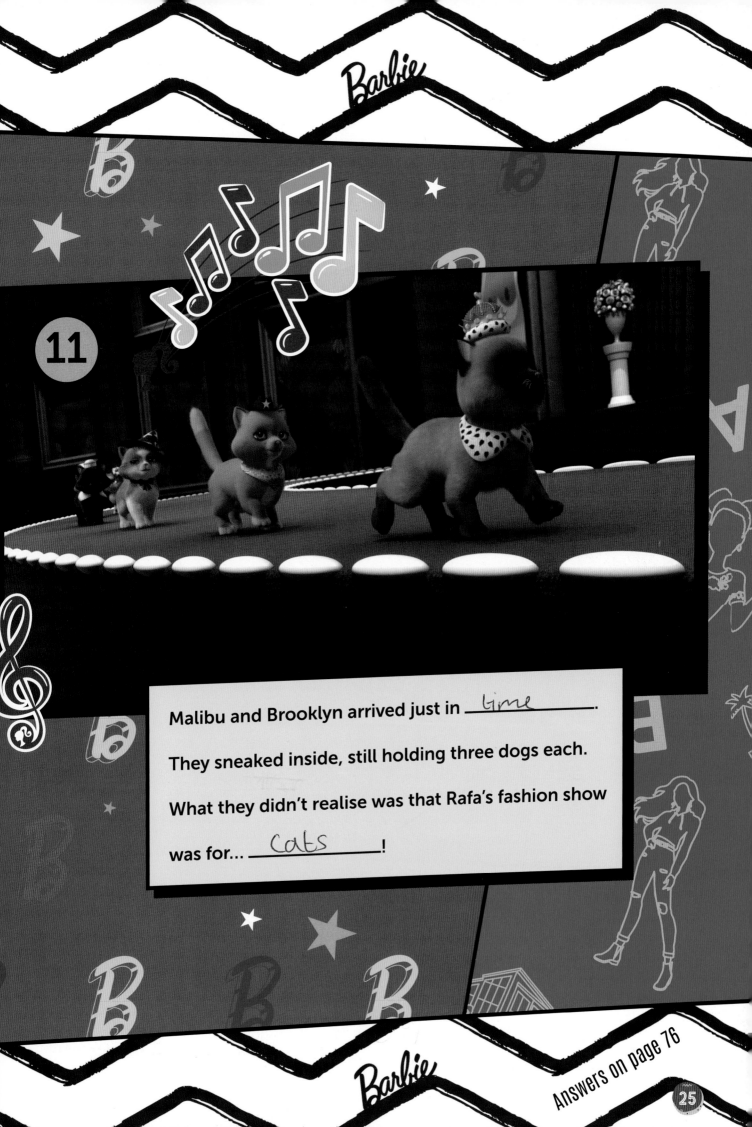

Malibu and Brooklyn arrived just in _time_.

They sneaked inside, still holding three dogs each.

What they didn't realise was that Rafa's fashion show

was for... _cats_!

Answers on page 76

12

Ruff, ruff!

The friends breathed a sigh of relief as each of the dogs slept through the ___show___ without a single bark at the fashionable felines on ___stage___. Unfortunately, when Rafa came out to take a bow with Gato, it was a different story...

13

Gato and the rest of the dogs began ___chasing___ each other all around the fashion show! They caused so much damage that Brooklyn and Malibu ended up giving all their dog walking money to Rafa to ___pay___ for it.

Barbie

14

Brooklyn and Malibu soon realised they needed more

help. In fact, they needed a manager and they

knew exactly who. Rafa! "How much does it pay?" Rafa

asked. "I can pay you in _food_," replied Brooklyn.

"Technically my parent's food." "Sold!" said Rafa.

Answers on page 76

THE END

MY 🌍 WORLD: Barbie ™

MY WORLD!

Full Name: Barbie Roberts

Also known as: Brooklyn!

Where I live: Born and raised in NYC!

My favourite things: Music, of course, dancing and acting.

My Parents

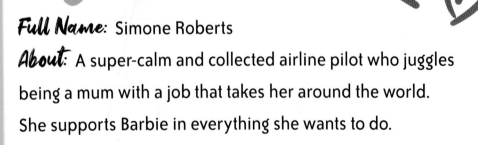

Full Name: Simone Roberts

About: A super-calm and collected airline pilot who juggles being a mum with a job that takes her around the world. She supports Barbie in everything she wants to do.

Full Name: Kelvin Roberts

About: Behind his serious architect exterior, Kel is a fun-loving dad who loves to cook and share his record collection with anyone who wants to listen!

MY FRIENDS

Full Name: Rafa
About: With his dog Gato, Rafa loves nothing more than hanging out with Brooklyn and Malibu and helping create their onstage outfits.

Full Name: Lyla
About: Lyla knows everything there is to know about music – and she knows what she likes. Without her, Blown Speaker Studios would have probably shut down years ago!

Full Name: Epiphany
About: Not only can Epiphany whip up the best coffee in New York, she can also read your aura. She's so in-tune, she can even tell if one of the diner chairs is feeling bored!

MY NEIGHBOURS

Jayla & Jackson are twins with big personalities. They live next door to Brooklyn with their adoptive dads and often come over to check out what Brooklyn is up to.

Mindful moments
CREATIVITY

Have you ever noticed how calm you feel when you are drawing or colouring? That's because your mind is focussed on one, fun thing! Try these mindful activities.

Take a line for a walk

- Place a piece of paper sideways.

- Starting halfway down, draw a line from one side of the paper to the other, taking your line for a walk! You can do squiggles or zig zags, loops or spikes. Wherever you want your line to go.

- With pens or pencils, follow the line you made, building up the pattern as you go. You can use any colours you want.

- Carry on until the page is full.

Colouring

- As well as the colouring pages in this book, there are thousands of colouring pages to download online.

- If you have a smartphone, there are lots of free colouring apps, which are also great for clearing your mind.

Doodle your thoughts

 Take a pen and a piece of paper and just draw whatever comes into your mind. It can be as detailed or as simple as you like.

 After a few minutes, take a look at what you have done.

Take time to make your soul happy

Pebble art

 This one is perfect if you are at the seaside or in your garden.

 Collect pebbles of all different shapes and sizes.

 Find a flat surface and start to arrange your pebbles into a shape or picture. It could be as simple as a spiral or heart shape!

PUPPY PALS

Barbie and her sisters love nothing more than playing around with their sweet puppies. Can you spot each of these super close ups in the big picture?

FORWARD FASHION

Malibu and **Brooklyn's** friend Rafa would totally *love* this fashion designer's studio! Take a look at this picture for 30 seconds, then turn the page and see if you can answer all of Rafa's questions... without looking back!

Rafa has *lots* of questions about the *fashion designer's studio*. How many can you get right without looking back?

1 How many cushions were on the sofa?

2

2 What colour was the sewing machine?

pink

3 Was there any yellow thread on the shelf?

yes

4 Was the roll of fabric on the table spotted or striped?

yes

5 How many bobbins of thread were on the table?

4

6 Were the ceiling lights silver or gold?

yes

7 Did the window overlook the city or a park?

yes

8 How many drawers were in the table?

2

Answers on page 76

PARK RUN

Help Malibu and Brooklyn find all the dogs in the park before it is time to return them to their owners!

START

FINISH

Answer on page 76

SHOW TIME!

Brooklyn and Malibu are finally ready to perform their music to an audience! Use the space below to design two outfits for their concert.

JAYLA AND JACKSON'S NEW FRIEND

Brooklyn's neighbours are always finding new pals to play with. Connect the dots to discover who they have met today!

Race to Blown Speaker!

Time is running out for Brooklyn and Malibu! They need to get to Blown Speaker Studios before Lyla closes up.

WHAT YOU NEED

- Dice
- A flat surface
- Two counters (these can be coins, buttons, small toys)

AIM OF THE GAME

Get Brooklyn and Malibu to the studios before the clock is filled!

HOW TO PLAY

1. Decide if you want to play as Malibu or Brooklyn (if there are more than two players, team up to make two teams)

2. The person who last listened to music goes first.

3. Roll the dice along the board on the next page.

4. If you land on a square with instructions, you must do what it says.

5. If you land on a clock square, you must shade in one quarter of the clock.

6. Both players / teams must reach the studio before all quarters of the clock are filled in!

7. If all quarters of the clock are filled in before you both reach the studio — time's up!

20
CLOCK

21
Is your t
nearly
Move bac
space

19

18
You're really
picking up speed
– roll again!

17
CLOC

3
Epiphany gives
you snacks for
the session!
Move forward
two spaces.

MALIBU

4
CLOCK

7

2

1
START

5

6
STOP to tie
your shoe!
Move back one
space.

Mindful moments
MEDITATION

Meditation has been used for thousands of years to help keep the mind and body healthy. Find a quiet spot to try out these simple techniques.

The seaside story meditation

- Sit in a comfy position or lie down.

- Close your eyes and breathe slowly in through your nose and out through your mouth.

- Imagine you are on a trip to the seaside. The beach and sea can be anywhere you like, real or imaginary.

- Think about what the weather is like. Is there a breeze? Is it warm? Think about what you can see all around you, what you can hear and even what you can smell.

- After a few moments, imagine you are leaving the seaside, then slowly open your eyes.

This meditation helps you to feel calm and happy

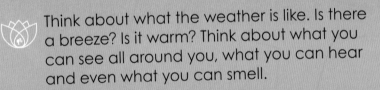

The whole-body meditation

🪷 This one works best when you are lying down.

🪷 Breathe slowly through your nose and out through your mouth.

🪷 Start by wriggling your toes, then letting them rest. Now, wiggle your feet, then let them rest.

🪷 Move all the way up your body, thinking about each part as you go.

This mediation is great at getting rid of nerves!

3 things meditation

🪷 This meditation is perfect to do out and about. It's a great way to calm your mind and ease your worries.

🪷 Start by taking deep breaths through your nose and out of your mouth.

🪷 Now, think about your senses. Look around you and name three things you can see. It could be a tree, a chair, the sky – anything!

🪷 Now think about three things you can hear. Then three things you can feel and three things you can smell (this might be quite tricky so don't worry if you only smell one or two things!)

This meditation is great for keeping you calm

You can be a Firefighter

It was a beautiful sunny morning in California. Brooklyn had come to stay with Malibu and her family for the weekend – Malibu couldn't wait to show Brooklyn all the sights of her hometown.

Soon, they stumbled across a community fair. There were lots of stalls selling locally-grown food, as well as people who take care of the community.

"I love meeting new people," said Brooklyn. Just then, she spotted a happy-looking dalmatian. "And it looks like we're not the only ones!"

The friends went over to say hello to the friendly dog. They soon realised that he belonged to the local fire station. "Hi," said a woman in a firefighter's uniform. "I'm Fire Chief Elena and this is Frankie, the firehouse dog."

Chief Elena began to show Brooklyn and Malibu all the ways the fire station help people in their community. "It must be so exciting to be a firefighter," said Malibu.

"It is," replied Chief Elena. "We get to do all kinds of things, but today we are teaching people about fire safety."

Brooklyn and Malibu listened carefully as Chief Elena explained how important it is to make sure your home has smoke alarms fitted – and to test them regularly. She also taught them how to make an 'exit plan' with their families.

"An exit plan includes different ways to exit each room of your home if there is a fire," explained Chief Elena. "And agree on a safe meeting point outside."

The friends agreed to make exit plans with their families as soon as they got home. "If you'd like to learn more about fire safety, come by the station," said Chief Elena. "I'm sure Frankie would love to see you again!"

The next morning, Brooklyn and Malibu couldn't wait to show Chief Elena the exit plans they had been working on. Brooklyn called her parents over video chat and worked out a plan for their home in New York, too.

"Welcome girls!" said Chief Elena as firefighters bustled around her. "Today we are checking all of the equipment in our fire engines and fire trucks."

Brooklyn and Malibu said they would love to help out, so Chief Elena gave them a list of jobs to do.

First, they helped to store the hoses and make a list of all the equipment in the engines and trucks.

Next, they washed a fire engine and took it in turns to see what it was like in the driver's seat.

Chief Elena showed Brooklyn and Malibu where the firefighters keep their protective clothing. "Firefighters wear special gear," Chief Elena explained. "We need protection from fire as well as heat, chemicals, water and electricity."

The clothes were laid out ready for the firefighters to put on as quickly as they can. "When the alarm rings, we need to get dressed in less than a minute!" said Chief Elena.

"I might try this at home to get ready for school faster," Brooklyn joked.

At that moment, the fire alarm sounded, and the firefighters jumped into action. "There must be an emergency," Brooklyn said to Malibu.

Chief Elena let the girls ride along in the fire engine, as long as they promised to stay safe. Brooklyn and Malibu were very excited – and when they arrived at the scene, they could see a thick plume of smoke rising into the sky.

As the firefighters rushed towards it, they soon saw that it was just a garden barbeque. "I'm sorry," said a man, looking a bit startled to see firefighters in his back garden. "I had put some burgers on the grill and then went inside to get hot dogs. The grill caught fire while I was gone, but I was able to successfully put it out."

Chief Elena reminded the man that the best way to stop a fire is to prevent it from happening in the first place. The man thanked the firefighters and asked if they would like to stay for a burger. "That sounds great, but we'd better get back to the station," Chief Elena said.

Back at the station there was one more job that Brooklyn and Malibu wanted to help with. Making dinner for the team! "We know exactly what will hit the spot," Brooklyn said with a grin. "Burgers!"

THE
END

FRIENDSHIP
HEROES

Malibu and Brooklyn are ready to be brave and safe as firefighters!

SWEET 'N' FRESH!

Smoothies are a delicious way to stay healthy and hydrated!

!
Ask a grown-up to help.

INGREDIENTS

- 200g frozen berries
- 150mls Greek yogurt
- 1 ripe banana
- 230mls orange juice

TIP
Replace the Greek yoghurt with dairy free yoghurt to make it vegan.

TIP
Add a tablespoon of your favourite nut butter for a salty hit.

WHAT TO DO

1. Place all the ingredients in a blender and whizz up to make your smoothie!

ANIMAL CARE

It's a busy day at the vet's clinic. Brooklyn and Malibu have a lot of animals to care for.

TAKE A LOOK AT THIS PICTURE OF THE SURGERY'S WAITING ROOM TO SEE IF YOU CAN SPOT 6 DIFFERENCES BETWEEN THEM.

Answers on page 77

VET CLINIK

Colour in a heart for each difference you spot!

57

FRANKIE SPOT!

Frankie, the fire station's trusty Dalmatian, is always on hand to help - and sniff out the best sausages at a BBQ! Can you find which Frankie is the right one?

1

2

3

4

5

6

Firefighter Fun!

What can you remember about Brooklyn and Malibu's day at the firestation?

1 WHAT WAS THE NAME OF THE FIRE CHIEF?
- (a) Emily
- (b) Elena
- (c) Emma

....

2 WHAT COLOUR COLLAR DOES FRANKIE WEAR?
- (a) Blue
- (b) Red
- (c) Green

....

3 HOW LONG DO THE FIREFIGHTERS HAVE TO GET DRESSED WHEN THERE IS AN EMERGENCY?
- (a) 10 minutes
- (b) 7 minutes
- (c) 1 minute

....

4 WHAT WAS THE EMERGENCY?
- (a) A cat was stuck up a tree
- (b) A barbeque had set on fire
- (c) A lift had broken down

....

5 WHAT DID BROOKLYN AND MALIBU COOK FOR THE FIREFIGHTERS' DINNER?
- (a) Burgers
- (b) Hot dogs
- (c) Spaghetti

....

Answers on page 77

BOOKS, BOOKS, BOOKS!

Barbie and her sisters love doing different activities, but one thing they all agree on is books! They love to share their favourites with each other and always read a few pages before bedtime. Use this page to share all the books you love!

MY FAVOURITE BOOK
crease + fold

THE BOOK I WANT TO READ NEXT
a fashion book

The first book I remember reading
The naughet unicorn christmas

IF I COULD BE ANY CHARACTER FROM A BOOK IT WOULD BE
Holly hills

THE BEST FILM BASED ON A BOOK
diary og a wimpy kid Rodrik rules

Use this space to design the front cover of your dream book.

PERHAPS IT'S THE BOOK YOU WILL WRITE ONE DAY?

Nature search

Barbie loves learning about all sorts of animals. Can you find all the creatures listed below in the grid?

S	D	F	L	F	G	H	T	Y	T
S	D	M	A	I	T	I	L	T	O
V	S	D	Q	U	O	E	E	I	R
B	N	S	T	R	E	N	E	G	T
M	O	N	K	E	Y	E	T	E	O
O	G	H	F	D	E	D	S	R	I
U	C	V	B	E	A	R	S	G	S
S	D	H	J	Y	T	Q	W	E	E
E	E	O	S	M	A	A	E	F	G
F	G	E	G	X	C	V	C	N	M
Q	W	E	R	T	I	B	B	A	R
G	O	R	F	H	Y	U	I	O	P
K	A	N	G	E	R	O	O	X	C

Tip
Look across, down and diagonally.

BEAR
CAT
DOG
FROG
KANGEROO
LION

MONKEY
MOUSE
RABBIT
TIGER
TORTOISE

Answers on page 77

BIKE RIDE

Skipper and Chelsea are off on a ride!

Take a look at this picture and see if you can work out all the missing pieces!

1

2

3

7

6

5

4

Answers on page 77

63

Your story!

Can you tell what's going on in this story?

Look at the pictures then write what you think is happening underneath!

Tip

Look at all the pictures before you start your story!

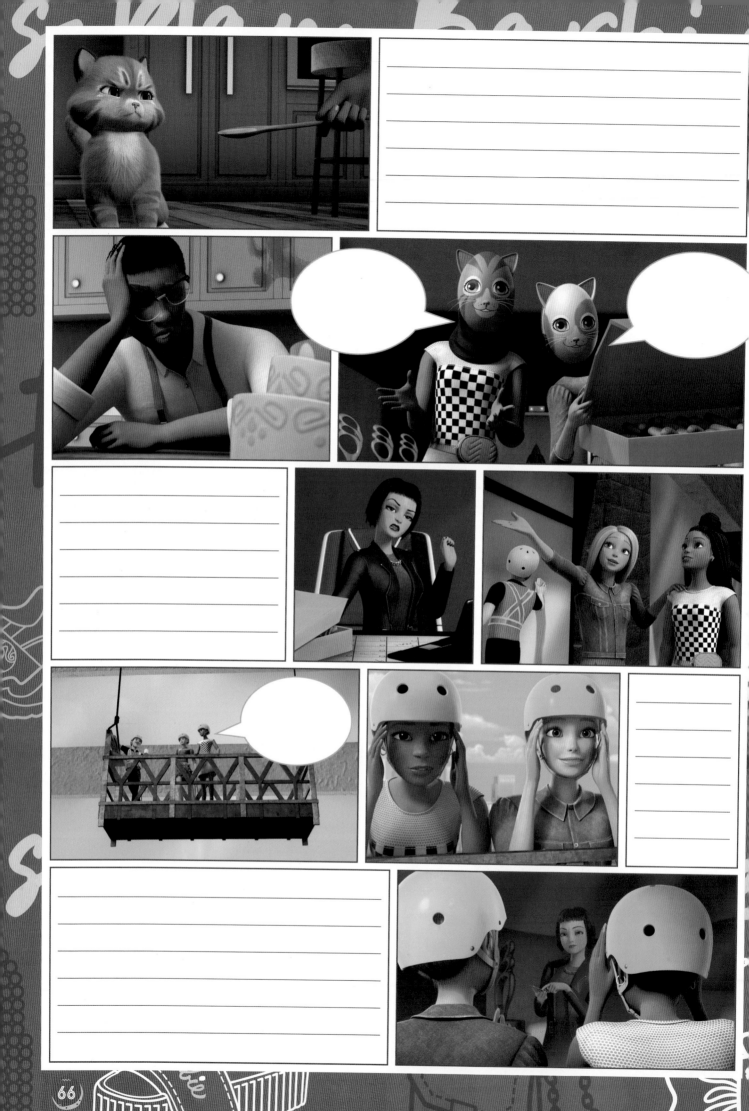

The end.

Mindful moments
ACTIVITIES

Mindfulness isn't just about being still and relaxing, you can be mindful when you are active, too!

Walking

If you are on a walk with your favourite pooch, or helping your parents with the shopping, you can also take a mindful moment.

Think about each step you are taking and how your foot feels on the ground. Is it hard or soft? Cold or warm?

Try to match your breathing to your steps – breathe in for two steps and out for two steps.

Notice what is around you. If you are outside, look for details in the sky or on trees or buildings. If you are inside, focus on something you like in the room you are in.

Tidying up

Even chores can help to keep your mind healthy!

Take your time. You might want to get your tidying chores done in super-quick time but slowing things down will really help! Think about how you are folding your clothes or smoothing down your bed. You'll find your mind becomes calmer as your room gets cleaner!

Homework

If you have a big project due, focus your mind with these mindful ideas!

 Before you start, take three deep breaths in and out.

 Set your working area out with everything you think you will need. Hold each pencil and pen to find the ones that feel best.

 Think about what you can hear and see. If it's a nice day, why not have the window open to get some fresh air and birdsong.

 As you are working, think about the sounds your pen or pencil makes on the paper. Take your time.

Crafts

Making things is a great way to focus and calm your mind!

 Friendship bracelets – making a bracelet for your BFF takes time and repetition. Whether it's lacing beads or knotting threads, this activity will totally zen you out.

 Painting – whether splashing paint onto a canvas or swooshing gentle watercolours onto paper – it's great for relaxation and mindfulness.

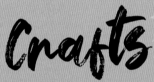

I'M WITH THE BAND!

Brooklyn and Malibu are on the lookout for a super-talented team to help them achieve their musical dreams! What would you do? Answer the questions to find out!

1 You've got rehearsals all day, what's the first thing you put in your bag?
- **a** Your music
- **b** Your diary
- **c** Comfy shoes

2 It's nearly time for your first show – what are you doing backstage?
- **a** Tuning your instrument
- **b** Making sure everyone is ready
- **c** Stretching and warming up your voice

3 What would be your go to on-stage outfit?
- **a** Something cool and comfy
- **b** Black, I don't want to stand out
- **c** Full-on glitz and sparkle

4 Everyone loved the show! What's the first thing you do when you come off stage?
- **a** Put your music away then celebrate!
- **b** Ask all your friends and family what they thought of the show.
- **c** Jump up and down with excitement

5 What would be the most important thing about being in Brooklyn and Malibu's band?
- **a** Making great music!
- **b** Being a hit!
- **c** Having fun!

6 The band have been asked to do another show! What's your first thought?
- **a** Let's write a new song!
- **b** Let's start making posters!
- **c** Let's work out a new dance routine!

MOSTLY As
YOU'RE IN THE BAND!
You love making music, so playing an instrument in the band would be your perfect role.

MOSTLY Bs
TALK TO MY MANAGER
Looks like you'd be great at organising The Barbies as well as everyone else. Watch out Rafa – you've got competition.

MOSTLY Cs
I'LL SUPPORT YOU!
Whether it's dancing or singing, you would support Brooklyn and Malibu with your amazing performance skills!

Sister Visit

Skipper has come to stay with Brooklyn and Malibu!

Can you work out which of these shadows matches the picture perfectly?

A

B

C

D

Answer on page 77

CROSSWORD PUZZLE

Answer the questions to fill in the grid on the opposite page.

Tip
If you can't think of an answer, move onto the next clue.

Tip
All the answers can be found somewhere in your book!

Answers on Page 77

Crossword puzzle answers:

1. (Down) m i c r o p h o n e
2. (Across) P i n k
3. (Across) r o b e r t s
4. (Down) s i m o n e
5. (Across) N e w y o r k
6. (Across) c h e l s e a

ACROSS
2. What colour hair does Daisy have?
3. What is Malibu and Brooklyn's surname?
5. Where do Brooklyn and Malibu live and study?
6. What is the name of Malibu's youngest sister?

DOWN
1. What do Malibu and Brooklyn sing into to make their voices louder?
4. What is the name of Brooklyn's mum?

73

MAKE A SKIRT!

Make a new skirt for Barbie to wear!

1. Copy the template on the opposite page onto plain paper or wrapping paper.

2. If you only have plain paper, now's the time to get creative and draw a pattern!

3. Start by folding along the first dotted line.

✂ Cut along the dotted line

! Ask a grown-up to help with cutting out.

! Make sure you have read page 73 before you cut up your book. Alternatively, copy or trace over onto plain paper.

TEMPLATE

4) Now, fold along the next dotted line, the opposite way.

5) Keep folding one way, then the other, until you have reached the last dotted line.

6) Now, fold in half and use a glue stick to keep the ends together.

7) Cut out the picture of Barbie on the opposite page, then use your glue stick to glue on the skirt and complete your design.

ANSWERS

PAGE 13

1 Brooklyn's phone

1 - Hey Malibu! Rafa said to meet at the cafe at 1pm. He has exciting news?

2 - Ooh what is it?

3 - Our new stage outfits!

4 - Can't wait to look fabulous!

2 Malibu's phone

1 - Hey Brooklyn what time is the studio booked?

2 - 3pm, but we have to be quick!

3 - Why?

4 - We only have it until 4pm!

PAGE 16

2 4 6 3 1 5

PAGE 18-27

1 - Brooklyn, song

2 - door, happy

3 - demo, York

4 - Rafa, one

5 - school, Malibu

6 - Speaker, smiled

7 - leave, $150

8 - fast, walk

9 - money, walking

10 - dogs, fashion

11 - time, cats

12 - show, stage

13 - chasing, pay

14 - help, food

PAGE 32

PAGE 34

1. There are 2 cushions on the sofa.

2. The sewing machine is pink.

3. Yes, there was yellow thread on the shelf.

4. The fabric is spotted.

5. There are 4 bobbins on the table.

6. The ceiling lights are silver.

7. The window overlooked the city.

8. There are 2 drawers in the table.

PAGE 35

PAGE 56-57

PAGE 58

Number 5 is the right Frankie.

PAGE 59

1 - b, 2 - a, 3 - c, 4 - b, 5 - a

PAGE 62

```
S D F L F G H T Y T
S D M A I T I L T O
V S D Q U O E E I R
B N S T R E N E G T
M O N K E Y E T E O
O G H F D E D S R I
U C V B E A R F G S
D H J Y T Q W E F G
E E O S M A A E F G
F G E G X C V C N M
Q W E R T I B B A R
G O R F H Y U I O P
K A N G E R O O X C
```

PAGE 63

PAGE 71

C is the correct shadow.

PAGE 72-73

```
          M
      P I N K
      I
      C
      R
      O B E R T S
      P           I
      H           M
  N E W Y O R K   O
      O           N
  C H E L S E A   E
```